Getting a Job

Building Bridges Series

Building Bridges Series: Getting a Job
Text by Catherine White
Illustrations by Marta Kwasniewska

First published and distributed in 2017 by Gatehouse Media Limited

ISBN: 978-1-84231-175-2

British Library Cataloguing-in-Publication Data:
A catalogue record for this book is available from the British Library

Jamal needs some extra money.
He wants to get a job in the computer shop.
He goes to the computer shop
and asks to speak to the manager.
"Do you need a part-time worker?" he asks.
The manager says, "Maybe. Give me your CV
and I'll think about it."

The next day, Jamal has some free time
at college.
He goes to the library to use the computer.
He starts to write his CV.
He lists his contact details.
He lists his education and skills.
He lists his experience and interests.
He prints out a copy to hand in
at the computer shop on his way home.

A few days later, he gets a call
from the manager of the computer shop.
The manager says, “Come in for an interview
on Friday afternoon at 4:30pm.”
Jamal is very happy.

On Friday afternoon,
Jamal puts on his best shirt, trousers
and jacket.
He cleans his shoes.
He combs his hair.
He looks very smart.

Jamal arrives at the computer shop
a little early.

The manager takes him into the office.
“Tell me about yourself
and why you want to work here,” he says.

The manager has seen Jamal
in the shop before.
He has seen Jamal looking at the computers,
the mobile phones and cameras.
Jamal is keen.
The manager likes that.
Jamal is polite and friendly.
The manager thinks Jamal will fit in well.

"I need extra staff on Saturdays.
I'll give you a trial," he says.
"You can start at 9 o'clock tomorrow
morning, if you like."

"Thank you, that's great," says Jamal.
"See you tomorrow."

Jamal leaves the shop

with a big grin on his face.

I must tell Ali, he thinks.

Maybe he can get a job there, too.

If you have enjoyed this book, why not try another title in the *Building Bridges Series:*

Going to College
Finding a Home
Going Shopping
Meeting Friends
Seeing the Doctor

Gatehouse Books®

Gatehouse Books are written for older teenagers and adults who are developing their basic reading and writing or English language skills.

The format of our books is clear and uncluttered.
The language is familiar and the text is often line-broken, so that each line ends at a natural pause.

Gatehouse Books are widely used within Adult Basic Education throughout the English speaking world.
They are also a valuable resource within the Prison Education Service and Probation Services, Social Services and secondary schools - in both basic skills and ESOL teaching.

Catalogue available

Gatehouse Media Limited
PO Box 965
Warrington
WA4 9DE

Tel/Fax: 01925 267778
E-mail: info@gatehousebooks.com
Website: www.gatehousebooks.com